CW00543030

CHART HITS

WISE PUBLICATIONS
PART OF THE MUSIC SALES GROUP

LONDON / NEW YORK / PARIS / SYDNEY / COPENHAGEN / BERLIN / MADRID / TOKYO

ALSO AVAILABLE IN THE *REALLY EASY PIANO* SERIES...

ABBA
25 GREAT HITS. ORDER NO. AM980430

BALLADS
24 CHART POP HITS. ORDER NO. AM982751

THE BEATLES
23 BEATLES HITS. ORDER NO. NO91080

CHRISTMAS
24 FESTIVE CHART HITS. ORDER NO. AM980496

CLASSICAL
36 POPULAR PIECES. ORDER NO. AM980419

ELTON JOHN
24 CLASSIC SONGS. ORDER NO. AM987844

FILM SONGS
24 SCREEN HITS. ORDER NO. AM980441

FRANK SINATRA
21 CLASSIC SONGS. ORDER NO. AM987833

JAZZ
24 JAZZ CLASSICS. ORDER NO. AM982773

POP HITS
22 GREAT SONGS. ORDER NO. AM980408

SHOWSTOPPERS
24 STAGE HITS. ORDER NO. AM982784

TV HITS
25 POPULAR HITS. ORDER NO. AM985435

60s HITS
25 CLASSIC HITS. ORDER NO. AM985402

70s HITS
25 CLASSIC SONGS. ORDER NO. AM985413

80s HITS
25 POPULAR HITS. ORDER NO. AM985424

90s HITS
24 POPULAR HITS. ORDER NO. AM987811

21st CENTURY HITS
24 POPULAR HITS. ORDER NO. AM987822

ALL TITLES CONTAIN BACKGROUND NOTES FOR EACH SONG PLUS
PLAYING TIPS AND HINTS.

PUBLISHED BY
WISE PUBLICATIONS
14-15 BERNERS STREET, LONDON, W1T 3LJ, UK.

EXCLUSIVE DISTRIBUTORS:
MUSIC SALES LIMITED
DISTRIBUTION CENTRE, NEWMARKET ROAD, BURY ST EDMUNDS,
SUFFOLK, IP33 3YB, UK.
MUSIC SALES PTY LIMITED
120 ROTHSCHILD AVENUE, ROSEBERY, NSW 2018, AUSTRALIA.

ORDER NO. AM993377
ISBN 978-1-84772-532-5
THIS BOOK © COPYRIGHT 2008 BY WISE PUBLICATIONS,
A DIVISION OF MUSIC SALES LIMITED.

MUSIC ARRANGED BY ZOE BOLTON.
MUSIC PROCESSED BY PAUL EWERS MUSIC DESIGN.
EDITED BY FIONA BOLTON.
COVER PHOTOGRAPHS COURTESY OF LFI.
PRINTED IN THE EU.

YOUR GUARANTEE OF QUALITY
AS PUBLISHERS, WE STRIVE TO PRODUCE EVERY BOOK TO THE HIGHEST
COMMERCIAL STANDARDS. THE MUSIC HAS BEEN FRESHLY ENGRAVED AND
THE BOOK HAS BEEN CAREFULLY DESIGNED TO MINIMISE AWKWARD PAGE
TURNS AND TO MAKE PLAYING FROM IT A REAL PLEASURE.
PARTICULAR CARE HAS BEEN GIVEN TO SPECIFYING ACID-FREE, NEUTRAL-
SIZED PAPER MADE FROM PULPS WHICH HAVE NOT BEEN ELEMENTAL
CHLORINE BLEACHED. THIS PULP IS FROM FARMED SUSTAINABLE FORESTS
AND WAS PRODUCED WITH SPECIAL REGARD FOR THE ENVIRONMENT.
THROUGHOUT, THE PRINTING AND BINDING HAVE BEEN PLANNED TO
ENSURE A STURDY, ATTRACTIVE PUBLICATION WHICH SHOULD GIVE YEARS
OF ENJOYMENT. IF YOUR COPY FAILS TO MEET OUR HIGH STANDARDS,
PLEASE INFORM US AND WE WILL GLADLY REPLACE IT.

WWW.MUSICSALES.COM

About You Now

Words & Music by Cathy Dennis & Lukasz Gottwald

Fizzing with synths, guitars, perky beats and a hypnotic chorus, this anthem for anyone who has thrown everything away and instantly regretted it became the sixth UK No. 1 for this century's most successful female act. Topping the chart on download sales alone, it achieved the biggest ever leap within the UK Top 40, from No. 35 to No. 1.

Hints & Tips: There is a lot of syncopation in this piece, apparent on a visual as well as audible level. As such, it is worth taking the time to look through the music before you play it, identifying how the steady crotchet pulse of the L.H. interacts with the off-beat rhythms in the R.H.

Beautiful Girls

Words & Music by Ben E. King, Jerry Leiber, Mike Stoller, Sylvester Jordan, Jonathan Rotem & Kisean Anderson

At the age of 18 years and seven months Miami-born, Jamaican-bred Sean Kingston become the youngest chart topper since Gareth Gates when, in September 2007, this track, which samples the Ben E. King classic *Stand By Me*, reached No. 1 in the UK charts.

Hints & Tips: Practise the L.H. on its own until you can play the repetitive rhythmic phrase confidently and securely. This will provide a steady bass line to which you can add the R.H. melody.

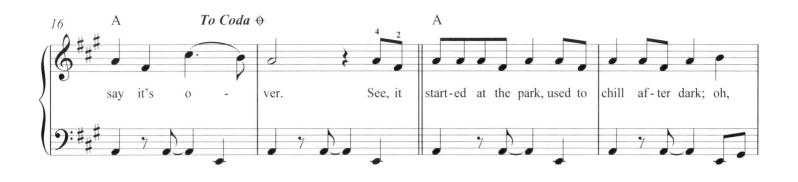

say it's o - ver. See, it started at the park, used to chill af - ter dark; oh,

when you took my heart, that's when we fell a - part, 'cause we both thought that love lasts for-ev-

- er.___ They say we're too young to get our-selves sprung; oh,

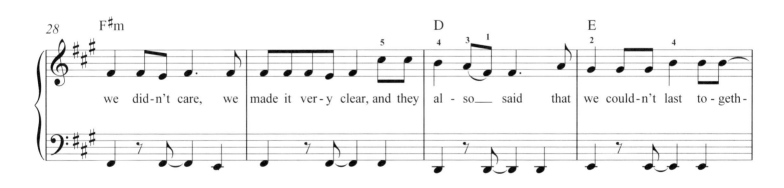

we didn't care, we made it ver-y clear, and they al - so___ said that we couldn't last to-geth-

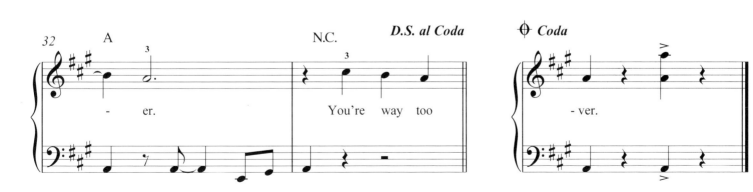

- er. You're way too

- ver.

BEYONCÉ & SHAKIRA

Beautiful Liar

Words & Music by Mikkel Eriksen, Beyoncé Knowles, Tor Erik Hermansen, Amanda Ghost & Ian Dench

No. 1 in the UK for three weeks, in the US this blend of American R&B and Colombian-Latin pop achieved the biggest ever upward movement on the Billboard Hot 100 by rising 91 places to No. 3 in April 2007. Nominated for two Grammies, it won the new MTV Video Music Award for Most Earth Shattering Collaboration!

Hints & Tips: This song also features a repetitive bass line, comprising a motif of just one bar in length, repeated throughout the entire piece. We call this an 'ostinato'. Its familiarity will tempt you to rush but try not to, not least because the R.H. has semiquavers to fit in!

Bleeding Love

Words & Music by Jesse McCartney & Ryan Tedder

The biggest selling UK single of 2007, recorded by the winner of the third series of TV talent show *The X Factor* and *Hello!* magazine's 2007 Woman of the Year, this song was the UK No. 1 single for six weeks and is included on Leona Lewis's debut album *Spirit*, the fastest-selling debut album ever in the UK.

Hints & Tips: It would be easy for this piece to sound mechanical by virtue of the very straight rhythms. However, you can avoid this and create an expressive performance by emphasising the most important note in each phrase. Underline the word in each phrase which you feel should carry slightly more weight, e.g. 'love' in bar 18.

Do You Know?

Words & Music by Enrique Iglesias, Sean Garrett & Bryan Kidd

Otherwise known as 'The Ping Pong Song' because of the sampled sound of a bouncing ball used as a percussion track, this was the first single taken from Inglesias's 2007 album *Insomniac*. It peaked at No. 3 in the UK, but in the US the Spanish version *Dimelo* totalled 11 weeks at the top of Billboard's Hot Latin Tracks.

Hints & Tips: Maintain a loose wrist and a light touch on the keys in order to achieve a bounciness that enables you to play the fast repeated semiquavers, particularly in bars 22 and 23.

Foundations

Words & Music by Kate Nash & Paul Epworth

A graduate of the BRIT School in Croydon, Kate Nash finished off some old songs whilst recovering from a broken foot, uploaded them onto *MySpace*, and soon found her career taking off. This song stayed at No. 2 in the UK singles chart for five consecutive weeks and was the lead single from her 2007 debut album *Made Of Bricks*.

Hints & Tips: Although the L.H. jumps around quite a lot in this piece, you can retain the same hand shape and simply move this up and down the keyboard as required. Practise this until you can judge the distances and thereby move to the correct positions without looking at your hand.

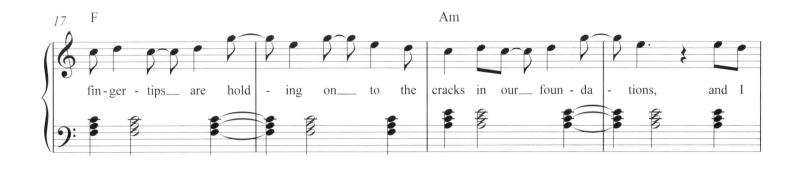

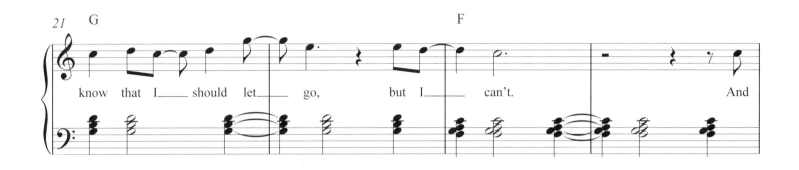

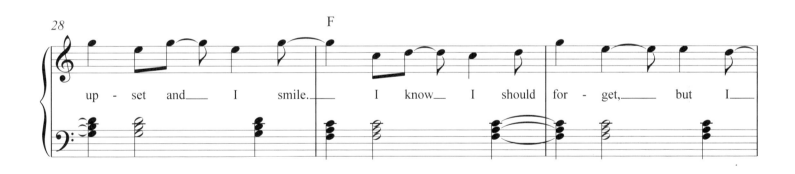

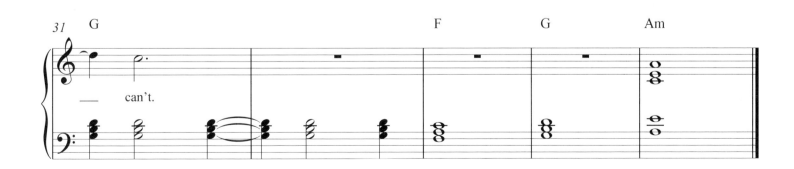

Goodbye Mr. A

Words & Music by Irwin Sparkes, Alan Sharland & Martin Skarendahl

This was the second single to be taken from The Hoosiers' chart-topping 2007 album *Trick To Life*. It is also one of 50 songs to be featured on the soundtrack of Electronic Arts' *FIFA 08* video game, band members Irwin Sparkes and Alfonso Sharlando having previously won football scholarships at the University of Indianapolis.

Hints & Tips: Create a punchy effect in the first half of the chorus (bars 17–27) by accentuating the crotchet octaves in the L.H. as indicated. Give them greater volume by attacking the keys with a mixture of speed and weight.

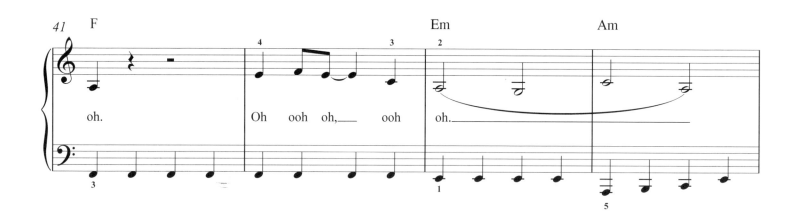

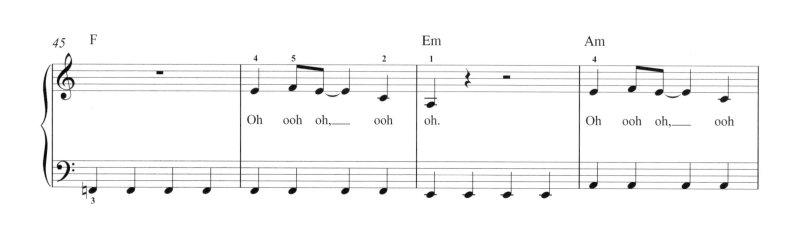

Lost

Words & Music by Michael Bublé, Alan Chang & Jann Richards

The composer describes this emotive ballad, one of two self-penned originals on his third studio album *Call Me Irresponsible,* as 'an anthem for star-crossed lovers' and 'my remark on the state of love'. Inspired by the break-up with his former fiancée, Bublé's spine-tingling vocal range combines gentleness with powerful expression.

Hints & Tips: This emotional song grows from a peaceful opening with semibreves in the L.H. (bars 1–8) through a passage with slightly more movement (bars 9–16) to the climatic chorus (bars 17–24) before dying away to a gentle ending. Reflect this with appropriate dynamics and perhaps by altering the tempo slightly too.

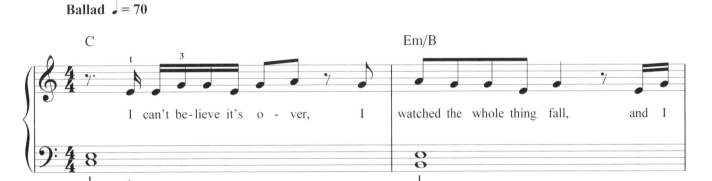

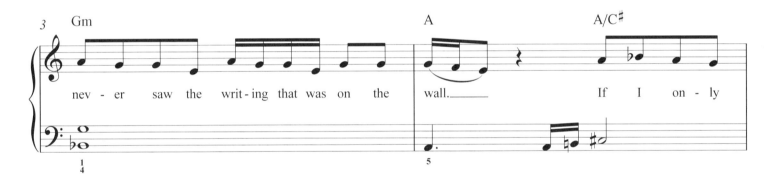

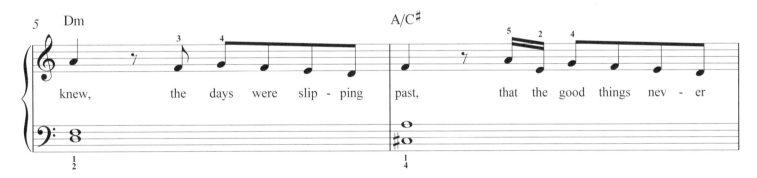

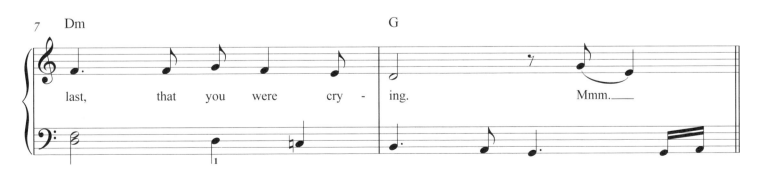

Headlines (Friendship Never Ends)

Words & Music by Emma Bunton, Geri Halliwell, Victoria Beckham, Melanie Chisholm, Matt Rowe, Richard Stannard & Melanie Brown

Following the band's decision to reunite, this was the Spice Girls' first single featuring the original line-up since Geri Halliwell left in 1998. Taken from their *Greatest Hits* compilation album, and selected as the official Children In Need single of 2007, the band performed it for the telethon, appearing live from Los Angeles.

Hints & Tips: The trickiest bar in this piece is probably bar 24, in which the L.H. takes over the melody. Practise this slowly, keeping your fingers close to the keys and trying to play it as smoothly as possible.

The time is now or nev - er to fit the miss - ing piece. To

take this on to - geth - er; you make me feel com - plete. We fall in - to the fu - ture, and

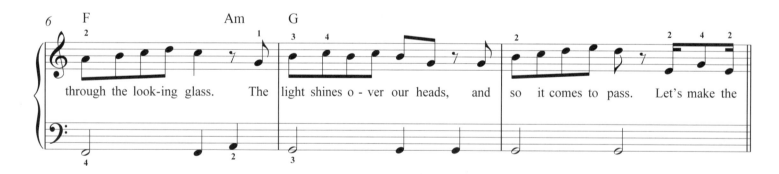

through the look - ing glass. The light shines o - ver our heads, and so it comes to pass. Let's make the

head - lines, loud and true. I wan - na tell the world I'm giv - ing it all to

you.   Let's make the   head - lines,   loud and clear._____   The

best things sud-den-ly hap-pen when you are   here.   If I   lost my way you'd car-ry me home, take me

all the way to heav-en, nev - er leave it   a-lone.   And it's   just like ev-'ry-thing mat-ters when you   are

near.   Let's make the   head - lines,   loud and true.____   Let's make the

head - lines, 'cause I'm giv-ing it all,_____   yeah, I'm giv-ing it all to   you._____

The Heart Never Lies

Words & Music by Thomas Fletcher

The youngest band since The Beatles to chart at No. 1 with their debut album, this was McFly's 13th single, their first contemporary rock ballad, and one of three brand new tracks on their *All The Greatest Hits* album. They first performed the song at the 2007 V Festival and were judged Best Pop Act at the UK Festival Awards that year.

Hints & Tips: Rotate your wrist from side to side, thus adopting a slight rocking motion to prevent your L.H. becoming stiff. Also ensure that this accompanying figure is played quite softly so as not to drown out the simple R.H. melody.

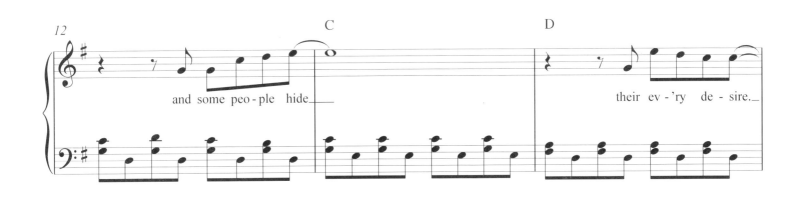

and some peo-ple hide___ their ev-'ry de-sire.___

But we are the lov-ers,

if you don't be-lieve___ me   when you look in -

-to my eyes,   'cause the heart___ nev-er lies.

Hold On

Words & Music by KT Tunstall & Edwin Makromallis

Variously described as an exhilarating three-minute ride and a thumping great hoedown, this was the first single release from Scottish-born KT Tunstall's third album *Drastic Fantastic*.

Hints & Tips: Practise the chorus (bars 17–24) hands separately, giving particular attention to the fingering in the R.H. If the stretches required are too large for your hand, just play the lower notes as these contain the melody.

Home

Words & Music by Michael Bublé, Alan Chang & Amy Foster Gilles

A cover of a ballad by Michael Bublé but with a slightly different lyrical arrangement, this was the first single to be released from Westlife's ninth studio album *Back Home*. It debuted at No. 3 in the UK singles chart in October 2007 and also appeared as the B-side on *The X Factor* winner Leon Jackson's 2007 Christmas No. 1.

Hints & Tips: Ensure that the last semiquaver of each two-beat group doesn't stick out by playing it with a slightly lighter touch and making sure you don't clip it. This will give the melody a 'cantabile' (singing) feel.

Hometown Glory

Words & Music by Adele Adkins

Following critical acclaim for this evocative portrait of all her fondest memories of London, at 19 years old, this Tottenham-born singer-songwriter and BRIT School graduate is already tipped for future success by topping the BBC's Sound of 2008 poll and being nominated as the BRIT Awards 2008 Critics' Choice.

Hints & Tips: The leaps in the L.H. might be too wide for your hand to span. If this is the case gently 'rock' between the two, playing each note for as near to its full length as you can.

1234

Words & Music by Sally Seltmann & Feist

Sales of this track and *The Reminder*, the album on which it appears, both rocketed following its use on the TV commercial for Apple's iPod Nano. Canadian Leslie Feist has since gained Grammy nominations for Best Female Pop Vocal Performance, Best New Artist, Best Pop Vocal Album and Best Short Form Music Video.

Hints & Tips: Give this piece a slight swing by making the first of each pair of quavers longer than the second, creating a rhythm reminiscent of the nursery rhyme *Humpty Dumpty*. If in doubt, try to listen to the track.

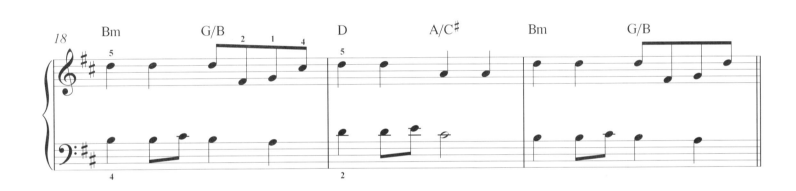

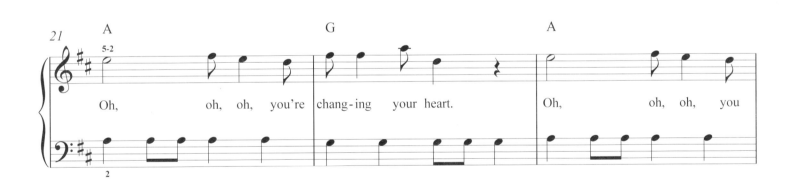

Read My Mind

Words & Music by Brandon Flowers, Dave Keuning, Mark Stoermer & Ronnie Vannucci

This Las Vegas-based rock band's lead vocalist Brandon Flowers deemed this the best song he'd ever written. It was widely praised, despite negative reviews for their album *Sam's Town*, from which it was the third of four tracks to be released as a single in the UK, NME describing it as a 'righteous and anthemic album highlight'.

Hints & Tips: Emphasise the first crotchet of eight (spread over two bars) to prevent this arrangement sounding monotonous and boring. Also bring out the chords (bars 10–11 and 14–16) and motifs (bars 26–27 and 30–31) that feature between the phrases to create extra interest.

MIKA

Relax (Take It Easy)

Words & Music by Nicholas Eede & Michael Penniman

Lebanese-born Mika studied at the Royal College of Music and performed classically at the Royal Opera House but failed to chart in the UK with this song on its original release. However, it gained widespread success throughout Europe following his early 2007 No. 1 hit *Grace Kelly*, and was re-released at the end of the year.

Hints & Tips: There are three sharps in the key signature of the piece. Familiarise yourself with playing so many black notes by practising A major scale (to which F# minor, the key of this piece, is harmonically related). The scale contains three sharps, namely F#, C# and G#.

KAISER CHIEFS
Ruby

Words & Music by Nicholas Hodgson, Richard Wilson, Andrew White, James Rix & Nicholas Baines

Taken from their second album *Yours Truly, Angry Mob*, in February 2007 this became the English rock band's first ever No. 1 hit and the year's tenth biggest selling UK single, particularly popular with chanting football fans. The band take their name from the South African club for whom former Leeds United defender Lucas Radebe played.

Hints & Tips: Similarly, practise A♭ major scale (to which F minor, the key of this piece, is harmonically related) to familiarise yourself with this key signature and the three flats (B♭, E♭ and A♭) it contains.

Rule The World

Words & Music by Mark Owen, Gary Barlow, Jason Orange & Howard Donald

Written especially for the movie *Stardust* starring Robert De Niro and Michelle Pfeiffer, and premiered at the 2007 National Movie Awards, this was the fifth biggest-selling UK single of 2007 despite never reaching No. 1. After rocketing up the charts from No. 46 it got stuck at No. 2 behind Leona Lewis for four consecutive weeks.

Hints & Tips: Listen carefully to the R.H. in the passage from bar 12 to the end, ensuring that the two notes sound together. Practise this separately if you need to.

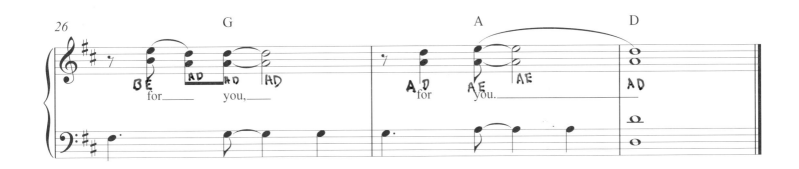

When You're Gone

Words & Music by Avril Lavigne & Butch Walker

This power ballad about being with someone you love and the little things you miss about them when you have to say goodbye, inspired by Lavigne's husband Deryck Whibley, was the second single taken from her 2007 album *The Best Damn Thing*, brimful of gutsy guitar riffs, singalong choruses and rebellious rock'n'roll attitude.

Hints & Tips: Even though the melody of this song contains several phrases with repeated notes, try to create a 'legato' (smooth) effect by holding each note for its full length.

ROBYN

With Every Heartbeat

Words & Music by Robin Carlsson & Andreas Kleerup

This collaboration with electronic artist and fellow Swede Andreas Kleerup blends the gritty sound of American R&B with the sunny pop of their homeland and was Robyn's second UK single, unexpectedly topping the UK charts in August 2007. Since her previous UK hit in 1998 Robyn had spent time as an ambassador for UNICEF.

Hints & Tips: Try playing the L.H. 'staccato' (indicated by the small dot under each note), meaning that the note is slightly shorter and more detached than normal. This will give the piece a light bouncy texture rather than it sounding too heavy.

Umbrella

Words & Music by Christopher Stewart, Terius Nash, Shawn Carter & Thaddis Harrell

This single was 2007's biggest seller on the United World Chart, spending seven weeks at No. 1 on the USA's Billboard Hot 100 and topping the UK Chart for ten consecutive weeks, the longest reign since Wet Wet Wet in 1994, and ironically at a time when the country was beset by extreme rainfall and flooding.

Hints & Tips: Although this piece is fairly straightforward, do practise it slowly at first, ensuring that the notes in the R.H. and L.H. sound at exactly the same time when they are supposed to—most of the time!

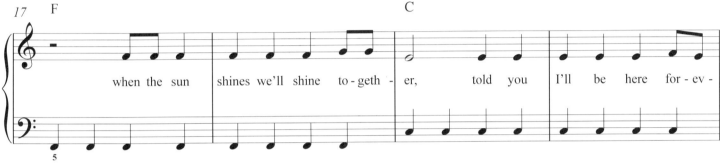

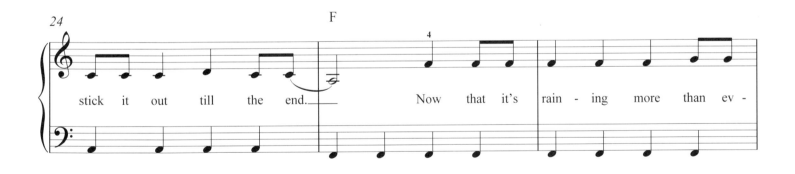

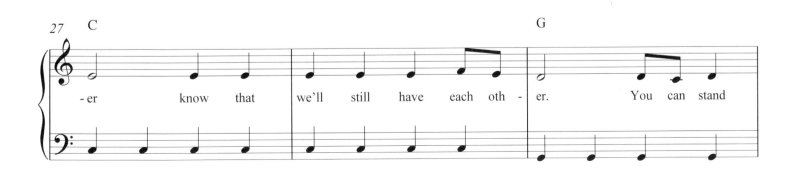

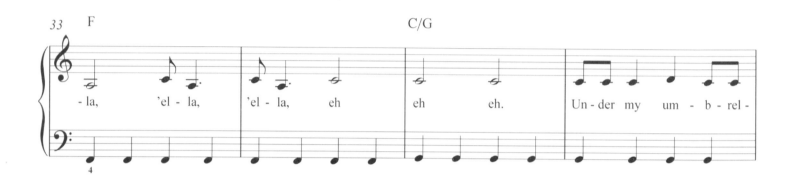

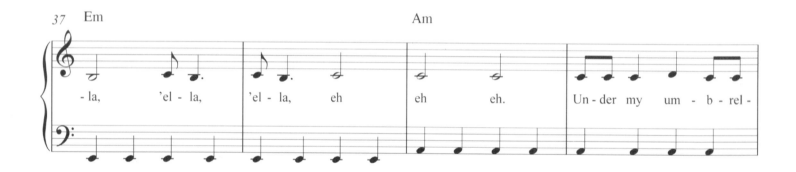

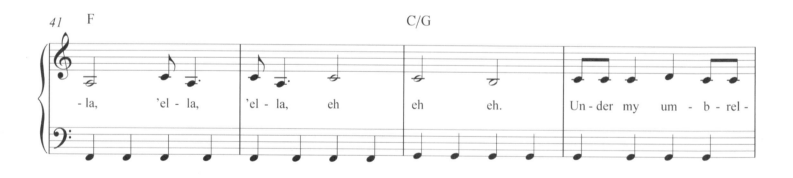

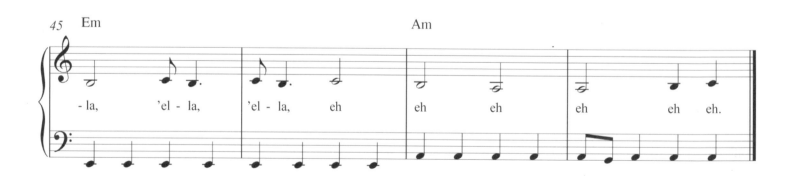

2/09 (168509) 4 5 6 7 8 9